ONCE UPON A TIME

IN THE

TEMPLE OF THE HATHORS

Nia Durward

DEDICATION

I dedicate this book to the beloved memory of James Tyberonn and Anne Meiklejohn Tipton.

They will always be remembered and missed by the family of Earth-Keepers they created. I am so grateful for all the love and wisdom they shared with us and for the transformative sacred journeys and spiritual events they lead for us.

SOPHIA - EGYPT

I awaken suddenly. What's that sound, a resounding male voice singing out in the distance like a bell or horn? Oh yes, it's the Imam's call to prayer. It must be 5 am. I feel charmed and compelled to sit up and meditate. I reach for my crystal, close my eyes and slip into a relaxed, appreciative, open state. I settle deeply into my body and root into my connection with the Earth. I breathe earth energy up through my body and into my heart. Then exhale up through my throat and out through the top of my head to connect with the Light of our Sun and the stars. I breathe Light down through my crown into my heart and send it through me back to the Earth. I have become an open channel between Earth and Sky. I settle into my heart, merging into feelings of Love and Oneness, as I breathe in energy from above and below, earth and sky, and breathe out love in ever-expanding waves of tenderness. Enveloped in this sweet, vast stillness, I feel open and receptive. I hear an inner voice say, "Tell Rose to find the 12th gate." I start to come out of my meditative state, remembering that I received this same message yesterday and the morning before that too! I must be meant to act on this in some way.

Rose is one of the new friends I've made on this trip. We're part of a group of about 100 on a sacred journey in Egypt. We have been sailing on the Nile for the past few days, but today we'll be back on land, boarding tour buses and heading out to sites in and around Luxor. Fortunately Rose is on my bus and I make a point to sit near her. I am excited to tell her this important message from my meditation.

But Rose just looks at me with a shrug and says, "Sophie, I don't have any idea what you're talking about. Are you sure the message is for me?" and turns around to talk to another friend about where to buy some snacks later.

Hmm, certainly not the response I expected from her. Yet, I feel more than ever that the message is important. Maybe the Hathors are trying to get my attention again. They certainly had a lot to do with my being in Egypt in the first place. And my middle name is Rose—Sophia Rose.

It was five years ago that I first heard of the Hathors. I had gone to get a psychic reading for the first time ever. The psychic suggested we do a little meditation together to start, and I easily sank into my usual heart meditation similar to what I described above. The first thing she told me after that was that her guides recognized me as connected to the Hathors and did I know about them? She seemed surprised that I'd never heard of them. Briefly she explained that they were connected with the ancient goddess Hator of Egypt but were actually interdimensional beings coming to earth to help us humans. I really didn't know what to do with this information. It took me a few more years before I was ready finally to learn more.

Then I found Tom Kenyon's website and was fascinated by his work with the Hathors and sound healing. I ordered his book The Hathor Material. I couldn't stop staring at the photo on the cover of a Hathor face from an Egyptian temple. It felt so loving and compelling. When I read about the meditation practice that they were suggesting for us, it was so familiar, essentially the heart meditation I'd been doing for years!

SOPHIA – ABU SIMBEL

About 6 months ago, I learned about this sacred journey to Egypt. I could not resist signing up for it, even though I didn't know anybody else participating. It must have something to do with discovering my Hathor connection, I imagined.

My suspicions were confirmed on the third day of our journey when we reached Abu Simbel on a beautiful lake above the Aswan Dam on the Upper Nile. What an experience to enter the smaller temple dedicated to Nefertari the wife of Ramesses II and encounter my first temple space filled with Hathor columns, each with a carved image of a Hathor face at the top. I was transfixed even more than when I first looked at the Hathor image on the cover of Kenyon's book. It seemed so obvious that these images are of star beings holding an expansive yet very gentle loving energy. I was guided to stand with my back against a column while facing the opposite one and looking into the Hathor's eyes. I experienced receiving a powerful initiation by the Hathors. My heart was filled with peace, joy and unconditional love. The energy was completely balanced, healing and restorative. I was told to use my heart to connect with this Hathor energy in my healing practice.

"Thank you for this blessing dear Hathors. Can you tell me more about your relationship to the Goddess Hator?"

"We are the Goddess Hathor. We chose to embody on earth in conjunction with the divine feminine in Her form. Hat = house, physical body, physical humanoid with extra terrestrial characteristics. Hor = sky god, Horus, stars. The myth was played out of an Egyptian goddess/princess mating with an elevated being from Sirius. The Divine Mother births her beautiful spiritual e.t./ human child. But also the rebirth process each initiate must go through," was the cryptic reply.

I was also given an assignment to go back to the main temple where I had earlier perceived a very wonky drowning energy and conjectured it was due to the fact that the original temple site was now underwater below the Aswan Dam. Returning to the temple, I found that, now full of Hathor energy, I was able to easily ground and balance the disturbed energy field.

SOPHIA – THE 12TH GATE

Finally our tour group arrives at the Karnak Temple Complex, and there I see a sign about the 12 Gates of Isis! I ask a guard "where is the 12th Gate?"

He gestures ahead and says, "the last one, at the end."

Of course! And I remember the story about Isis' journey through the 12 Gates of the Underworld to rescue her beloved Osiris. Leaving the rest of my tour group behind, I rush through the temple grounds down the walkway through the gates to the very end.

Standing there by myself, I am swept away by a wave of emotions, feeling the intense love between Isis and Osiris, the lover and the beloved. There is a touching of some long ago memory of such a union, such a feeling of transcendent merger into Oneness. I wander off in a hazy altered state, with a longing sense that my beloved is just out of reach but also ever-present in my heart. I find some broken pieces of temple off to the side and settle on a flat place to sit and meditate.

No sooner do I close my eyes, than a beautiful image of Isis appears in my inner field. She enfolds me in her winged arms and I am melted by her vast loving compassion. I feel completely healed and loved in Her embrace. Isis turns me so that my back is fastened to her front. She silently communicates to me that we are going on a journey and that I will be safely held this way. She stretches her wings and we take off, gliding over the Nile.

As we float over the Nile, I notice a small felucca far below on the water. I'm attracted to get a closer look and my desire seems to bring us closer. Riding inside is a beautiful young Egyptian princess. She seems dreamy and faraway. I find myself slipping into resonance with another timeline, another now.....

Once upon a time, along time ago, on the Nile. The Princess Niantha was gliding down the River in her boat. She was in a reverie, trailing her hand in the water.

"Where is he?" she wondered." "Where is the one I see in my dreams?

I hear him singing, calling to me. My heart is flooded with love and longing.

He feels so near, yet so far away. It is as if we've known each other always, but yet I don't know what he looks like, just how he feels. "Where are you? What is your name?"

And her thoughts trailed off as Niantha slipped deeper into a meditative state. When she resurfaced to normal consciousness and opened her eyes, she felt a lingering bliss and a deep knowing in her heart that she had been in loving communion with her beloved, her eternal soul mate. The mystery of his identity was not solved, but she was more certain than ever that he and their love are real.

And as Niantha resurfaced, I was again aware of myself flying with Isis now far above the Nile and heading for the mountains in the distance.

"We are here. Come to us little one. It is time." Beckoning voices are calling me.

Isis lands with me at the top of the mountains in somewhere somewhen that is warm and fragrant with beautiful humming, singing in the background. I am surrounded by many ephemeral figures, very tall and willowy. I feel completely safe and nurtured as I am lifted by many hands and placed gently into warm scented waters then washed and massaged all over. I am placed comfortably on soft cushions. Warm breezes and oil scented with frankincense and lotus flowers caress my body and senses. I relax deeply with quiet mind into a state of bliss.

I am vaguely aware of the continued attendance of the tall otherworldly beings as they sing to me, brush my hair and flow their hands through my aura. It feels as if they are making adjustments, fine tunings. I especially feel them around my head and vaguely wonder what they are placing there. This goes on for some time. Eventually, they seem to reach completion and hold a mirror up for me to inspect the results.

"Ohhhhh! Thank you." I can't help but smile at how beautiful I look. I am glowing with light and amazing crystals and jewels crown my head, scattered through my hair and floating in my aura.

Now I realize that the sweet beings who have been caring for me are Hathors and that I am fully resonating with their distinctive heart energy of love and healing. Isis, too, seems to vibrate with the Hathor heart energy. I slowly make eye contact with each Hathor in gratitude and farewell. Then allow Isis to attach my back to her heart. It is time for her to fly me back to the temple.

Soon I open my eyes to find myself sitting once again at the edge of the temple site, wondering how much time has gone by and hoping that my tour group is still there.

As it turns out, I easily find some of my friends from the tour and learn I haven't missed much. They share about an honoring ceremony they have performed, and I just tell them I've been meditating with Isis.

SOPHIA – DREAMING NIANTHA

That night as I lay in bed before sleep, I muse about the amazing experience I had at Karnak temple. I can still feel the blissful reverberations in my body and energy field. I find myself focusing on the image of the Egyptian princess in the felucca, wanting to know more about who she is. She comes to me in my dreams, saying:

I am called Niantha. I am the daughter of Theron. There is a great mystery around my birth. My father says I was born early at least one moon before anyone expected and exactly at the time of the full moon celebration of the Goddess Hator. My mother's pregnancy and my birth were easy. My mother was healthy and relaxed and blissfully happy the whole time. She was a priestess in the Hator temple and spent many hours there all during the pregnancy and went to the temple for my birth rather than have the midwife priestess come to our house. From the beginning I was a healthy and precocious child despite my early arrival. My parents named me Niantha but I was often teasingly called Hatti, child of the Goddess! I never got a chance to ask my mother about my birth story as she died when I was very young shortly after the birth of my younger brother.

It was expected that like my mother I would become a priestess of Hator. My father never remarried, and I felt like all the priestesses were mothers and older sisters. They dressed me up in little copies of their robes, fed me tasty treats left as offerings, and helped me memorize prayers to the Goddess. I loved their loving attention and the sweet atmosphere of the temple. Most of all I loved singing with them! At sunrise and sunset they sung the sun up and down. As the light played through the open temple, their voices elongated each vowel sound into a beautiful resonant tone. I could feel the tones vibrating inside of me. In my feet, at the base of my spine, in my belly, in my heart, in my throat, between my eyes and at the crown of my head—each tone seemed to know its place.

The dream is so vivid! I awake with the singing and toning still vibrating in my body and have a very blissful meditation. I have a feeling that this won't be the last of my encounters with the Egyptian princess.

I don't have to wait long. The very next morning in my meditation I again hear the beautiful singing and toning and am swept into Niantha's experience.

The scent of lotus is in the air. I walk into the inner sanctum of the temple as if floating on a river current--pulled by the stronger and stronger sweet scent. There--the high priestness is stirring the oil extraction in a big pot. The heavy sweet smell is making me dizzy. My sisters catch me and lay me gently down on the bed. It is my turn to be the diviner.

"Sh Hatti, sh let the lotus take you." I slip into trance with some barely conscious part of my mind wondering what I will be asked and what I will say. I sink deeper and deeper into my floating half-sleep.

From far away, I hear a voice calling to me, "Focus, listen!"

I realize that with a little effort I can and am penetrated and absorbed by the question: "who is to be the next King of Dendera?"

I open my eyes and see my beloved Horus looking at me. Is he to be the next King? But he's not human? He slowly blinks his beautiful eye at me.

I hear the words coming out of my mouth, sounding far away and with a strong, deep resonance unlike my normal voice —"the eye of Horus will appear to designate who is to hold the King's staff!"

As the priestesses surrounding me record this message, I drift deeper into a blissful sleep.

SOPHIA – DENDERA

After my experiences over the last couple days my anticipation for today's visit to the Hathor Temple at Dendera is running very high. I put on my favorite rose quartz necklace and the special one I received from my crystal healing teacher with a clear quartz point and moldavite. I had been wearing both when I had my experience at Abu Simbel.

The bus pulls up at the Hathor Temple site. I find myself slowly exiting and lagging at the back of the group as we move across the carpark and up the steps to the front of the large imposing temple. By the time I enter the temple I am on my own. And there they are—those beautiful Hathor faces atop twenty-four giant stone columns! I feel dwarfed and mesmerized by their size and power, but I also feel so lovingly held and peaceful.

I stop to look up and connect eye to eye with one of the images. Just like at Abu Simbel the energetic effect is riveting, like my kundalini and all my chakras are being activated and aligned, coursing with powerful life energy.

I feel directed to begin walking through the whole grand entrance hall up and down through every row of columns. I begin to hear a low humming and the elongated vowel sounds characteristic of the Hathor singing. I see a vision of ancient Egyptians bringing seriously ill patients on stretchers into this hall and moving them through all the Hathor columns in much the same way as I am walking now. I realize that this is a true place of healing and meant to be open to all even though the inner sanctums of the temple were only open to the priests and priestesses.

The strange and beautiful singing is filling my senses now, opening my heart and mind. My inner vision sees deeply into the vastness of space. My heart is calling for her counterpart.

And the answer is heard softly with deep resonance. "I am here. I am here."

I answer, in higher echo: "I love you, I love you."

We are one. We are flying/dancing together through all space and time. We are aware of so many beings of light all around us. Somehow we are separate and One. Such a wonderful feeling of freedom and union at the same time!

"The power of sound is immense. That is why our Hathor ears are so large and emphasized. We will teach you to sing. Don't be afraid. All is vibration. Sound clears, sound opens the doors of perception, especially the heart."

Yes, the sounds transport me to a place of pristine crystalline beauty--a temple space that seems to have organically grown as the crystals grew and formed this space in response to the voice of angelic beings.

"This feels like I'm in a different temple. Where are we?"

"Yes. We have taken you to Sirius. To our Hathor Temple there. It's name is not pronounceable in human language but is something like that buzzing sound you hear in your ears. Enjoy being present and let the new energetic programming happen. Did you feel that cellular shift?"

They are still singing and I want desperately to join them, but still feel inhibited. Their hearts are smiling, encouraging me to allow the tones to emerge. I join in, feeling the vibration and love even more deeply in my body, heart, soul. My sound blends, separates, blends. Even when I stop, I feel the change, the more aliveness. Now the crystalline shapes are shifting to form a perfect huge pyramid of crystalline light. I am in the pyramid. The pyramid is in me. The geometry amplifies the ability of the crystals to hold the sound. And the sound helps the crystals to create the geometry. Is this how the great pyramids at Giza were created? And I feel a sense of affirmation.

As the vision and music fade, I am standing again in the vast entry hall of the Hathor Temple. I feel so blissful and content it is hard to move on from this wonderful sacred healing space. But I can feel the Hathors nudging me forward. There is something else they want me to find. I am drawn through the next areas of the temple rather quickly. There are beautiful sculpted images on the walls, and on the ceiling in one area is an amazingly well-preserved painting of the goddess Nut in the night sky full of stars. But they are pushing me to keep moving.

I am surprised to find a small doorway at the rear of the temple and cautiously exit concerned that I might not be able to get back in. My heart leaps as I see a much smaller temple located a short distance behind the main one! It seems that's where I am to go. I walk around it to the entrance on the other side, but oh no! There are two guards blocking the way.

"Please can I go in," I say politely but they don't seem to understand English. I pause allowing myself to be calm and sink back into the loving Hathor energy from earlier. Somehow the energy shifts and the guards stand back, gesturing me inside.

It is a relatively small and gloomy space inside. My excitement has waned and I am wondering if this is really what I was meant to find. There is such a feeling of sadness in the air.

Then, internally, I hear: "Call Niantha with us. Niantha ! Niantha!"

"Sophie, Sophie is that you?"

"Yes, from this now in Dendera at the small temple behind the grand Hathor Temple."

"I am at my beloved temple where I was born in Dendera. You feel so close. I am having a bad day. I'm missing my beloved Horus and I just found out father wants me to stop spending all my time here at the temple and prepare for marriage. He insists I must marry Bagra, the elder King from the next city-state. It will make both their positions stronger. But he is horrid."

"Is there anyway that I can help you? Or can the Hathors help?"

"Who are the Hathors?"

"Oops! I guess I'm getting ahead of the story, if you don't know them that way. Have you visited the stars where Horus lives?"

"Only in my dreams. Oh, only if I could go there and be with my Horus and escape my father's control!"

"Hmm? There must be some way. Tell me more about your relationship with Horus and maybe we will see a clue."

"Well, it started about a year ago when I turned 12. Every night for a week, I was awoken well before dawn to the sound of the most beautiful and haunting singing—filled with compelling elongated tones—even more beautiful than at the temple. It was irresistible and I would find myself singing softly in answer. My body awakened in a rainbow of sensations, especially my breasts, womb and vulva. Every cell was bathed in Light and my heart opened like a lotus flower. As the singing became softer and softer, I was always lulled back to sleep. In the morning, it seemed like a very vivid dream with lingering delicious sensations in my body and a longing in my heart."

"At the end of the week, I awoke to the flowing of my first woman's blood. The priestesses at the temple had already told me to expect this and that when it happened, we would celebrate my womanhood. It was a wonderful and exciting time for me in the temple, but unfortunately it also meant my father started looking in earnest for a "suitable" husband."

"I continued to hear the singing in my dreams but not every night and occasionally in the temple or when I was alone on the river in my felucca."

"I gradually understood that I was hearing the voice of a young man of incredible light and began to fall in love. He encouraged me to join him in singing and toning. It felt like he was teaching me how to communicate in his music language of the stars. The more comfortable I got doing so, the more my dream vision opened up. I saw thousands of stars, swirling in different colors. I saw my beloved sometimes as a hawk flying through the stars, sometimes as a very tall man twice my height with beautiful almond eyes and large shell-shaped ears protruding from the sides of his triangular head. I was shown images of his home in the distant stars."

"Niantha, it seems like the singing and toning are key to your connecting with your beloved. Maybe if we try doing it together, we can create a solution to your problem. If you start, I will join in."

"Ok. I would love to share this special singing with you. It will bond our hearts and it will certainly make me feel better."

As Niantha starts to sing in her beautiful elongated tones with no real words, I feel my heart opening and a sense of floating and dancing through space and stars. I join in, allowing my voice to mirror and weave around hers without thought or control. It feels so free and joyful and yet very much that we are singing together!

Just like when I was on the mountaintop with Isis, I feel and see the tall Hathor figures all around me. Only this time one figure in particular stands out. He is very handsome and seems to be smiling right at Niantha. I realize he must be her Horus. I somehow know that he is very pleased that she has used the power of sound to call them in and that now she can see him with his people. But it is the whole group of Hathors who speak, explaining to Niantha and myself in words that we can each understand in our minds:

"Thank you for using sound to call us to you today. We can always be called from your heart, but toning from the heart will really open the channel. A crystal dedicated to the purpose will hasten and amplify even more."

"Niantha our dear little sister we love you and are so happy that you have allowed us into your heart. You are now one of us. You will be called Hathor one day as the vessel that brought this beautiful heavenly love onto planet Earth. And you will create a temple and mystery school to house and share our wisdom. The love you share with Horus, who is one of us, is personal but also a composite of the consciousness that is the Light of the Stars. Your esoteric experience and teachings will sift down to be told as a love story of Hathor and Horus, Sky God and Goddess of ancient Egypt."

"We understand that you have a problem--your father wishes you to make a marriage that is not in accord with your heart or your soul's purpose. You must escape and begin your goddess training very soon. We will help you all we can."

"Oh Sophie, thank you so much! I am filled with hope and joy now. I understand what I must do and that I can use the special singing that my beloved has taught me to get the help I need from him and his Hathor family. You are my Hathor sister. I will never forget you. I know in my heart that somehow you will be learning along with me and also sharing this Hathor wisdom with others."

"Yes, I think you are right dear Niantha. I will connect with you often in my meditation dear sister of my heart and thank you for sharing the love and wisdom you receive with me. May we sing together with our Hathors again soon!"

Wow, what an amazing experience! As I open my eyes, coming back into my normal awareness, I'm feeling nervous and self-conscious about the guards. Did they or anyone else hear me singing? Then I notice that the door has been shut, and I feel a shiver of fear. I knock on the wooden door and it opens. The guards smile mysteriously and gesture me out.

NIANTHA – ESCAPING DENDERA

My father's palace is abuzz with preparations for the wedding. Old Bagra is arriving tomorrow. Today I am to go into seclusion in the temple for my ritual cleansing and adornment. This will be my last chance to escape. I must not fail. My dearest friend Shanti, one of the young priestesses, has promised to help me and to accompany me. It is a five-day journey to the turquoise mines in the mountains. She grew up there and knows the way. We have been preparing for weeks, secreting food and male clothing to disguise ourselves for the journey.

I pick up my little crystal falcon (my most prized possession since I found it 2 years ago in the river reeds) and place it next to my heart in an inner pocket in my bodice. And the memory surfaces:

"Ni Ni" her brother calls to her. "Where are you?"

Niantha wants to brush him off; pretend she doesn't hear him. But Geo is her beloved little brother. What if he gets lost looking for her? So she goes back and takes Geo by the hand. Gesturing with her finger to her lips to be silent. They creep through the reeds beside the Nile. And she hears the noise again—a feint whimpering.

"Oh look Geo a baby falcon. Be still. Don't scare it."

Her heart fills with love and motherly feelings for this wee being. But then it looks her in the eyes, and she knows he is more than what he appears.

She pulls a small silver thimble out of her pocket and dips it into a nearby lotus flower floating on the marshy water. There is a little bit of flower-scented dew cupped in the flower and it fills her thimble. She offers it to the baby falcon. He dips his tiny beak into the thimble as if to drink. When he opens his beak, she hears a clink.

Then he makes a loud resounding "heruuuu!" And flies off.

Although Niantha is startled, she is certain that this mysterious encounter was a special blessing. She watches the beautiful bird-- now much bigger--spiral upwards wings spread wide. Then looks down to find a tiny bird shaped crystal in her thimble.

There's Shanti at the door now. "Come Princess Niantha. We must hurry to the temple to prepare you for your wedding!" she says cheerfully with a wink.

I take a moment for a loving connection with my beloved Horus and his Hathor family, and run out the door after Shanti.

We skip down the tiled corridors and out into the sunshine chattering gaily, but my stomach is a bundle of nerves. We move across the central plaza of Dendera. It is early and there are only women out fetching water from the well. I feel their love and admiration for me their princess but also their jealousy!

As soon as we enter the temple, I sigh with relief. This has always felt like home to me, and I know no adult male will dare to come into this sacred feminine space. It would bring bad luck to the marriage. I am quickly surrounded by the priestesses and they usher me into the sacred bathhouse. The water has been warmed and lovingly scented with fragrant oils and flowers. I remove my dress and sink in blissfully. But then I am swept by a wave of sadness, realizing how much I will miss this haven. Will I ever see it again once I leave?

That night, after everyone has long been asleep both in the temple and in the city, Shanti comes for me. We quickly and silently dress in simple boy's clothing, take up our cloth shoulder bags of provisions, and sneak out. We don't put on our sandals and scarcely breathe until we are well away from Dendera. It is so very dark and I am terrified that we will be attacked by robbers or get hopelessly lost. I could never do this without my loyal Shanti at my side.

Then I hear faint singing ahead of us and glimpse tall Hathor figures flitting through the palms and know that they will be there to help us and guide us.

In my heart I hear Horus calling me, "Hatti come. I love you!"

"I love you too my Heru! I am coming."

I remember the first time he called me Hatti during one of our sweet dream-like encounters.

"I was given the name Niantha at birth. What name did you receive from your parents?"

"It's not really pronounceable in Earth language. You would consider it a high-pitched sound or a bird call. Maybe a little like the cry of a falcon or hawk. The Egyptian word for hawk "heru" gives a sense of the sound. So maybe you could call me Heru and I would love to affectionately call you your pet name Hatti."

"Ok. Hatti and Heru it is. I so love just being with you in our blissful silent union, I hate to waste a minute of our time together chattering about mundane questions. But then when I am back home in my usual form and daily activities, I wonder about so many things and wish I had asked you all my questions."

"Hatti, my beloved, I am glad to know that you think about me when we are apart. I will try to answer any questions you have."

"Where do we meet?"

"Sometimes we are on our Hathor colony on Venus. Sometimes we are with my family in the crystal palace in the Sirius Star System. I hope someday to shift with you through the portal there to our ancestral home, which is located in another Universe."

As we trudge on through the dark, I wonder--am I on my way finally to be with my beloved Horus in his home in the stars? Will we be able to wed and live together? I can't imagine how this will happen. But my heart believes it will. A frisson of excitement shivers through me.

Shanti and I have been in our little hut near the turquoise mine for a few days resting from our journey and meeting with her uncles, aunts and cousins who live and work nearby. They are very kind and generous and understand how important it is that my presence remains a secret. They are very devoted to the Goddess and seem pleased to accept Shanti and I as her representatives.

Besides turquoise, they dig up a lot of chrysocolla, another copper bearing stone with a beautiful green-blue color. They love to sing when they work with the stones, getting them ready to transport into the city to sell. As I handle the stones, I am inspired to join them and soon find myself doing the singing/toning I learned from Horus and the Hathors.

Amazingly, the singing of the others begins to shift into resonance with my voice. It is so beautiful and heart opening. I feel like I am coming alive to the energy of the rocks and the mountain—communing with them! And then I realize that we have called in the Hathors and they are singing with us too. I see their tall beautiful forms all around us. In the days to come, I will come to know that I wasn't the only one to see them as I begin to find carved Hathor figures and faces around the village and brought to our hut as gifts.

As the Hathors drift off, I hear a message in my mind, "Niantha, it is time for us to begin to teach you. You have much to learn. Be alone and ready at dawn."

NIANTHA – HATHOR TRANING

Just before dawn, I arise silently and grab up the bag I had prepared the night before with my special stones, a bit of food and my warmest shawl. I let my feet guide me to the perfect spot, a small cave in the rocks. I sit down and close my eyes to wait in peaceful silence. Just as the first rays of the sun strike my face and I realize I have been guided to the perfect spot, I hear the call of a falcon—the distinctive "heruuuu..." that I associate with my beloved Horus. Next thing I know the two of us are embracing just in front of my little cave, standing in a column of light absorbed in our loving heart connection.

"I must leave you now to your teacher," smiles Horus as he kisses me and flys off once again in his falcon form.

What a blissful way to begin my Hathor education! All my nervousness about what the training will be has now dissolved.

I sit back in my little cave in the warm sunshine and take out my breakfast of bread and dates. I notice an old woman coming up the slope towards me. She is dressed in a simple cotton shift tied with a woven belt and looks much the same as Shanti's aunts though a bit older. I don't recognize her. She stops in front of me smiling, and I invite her to sit and share my food. As we quietly munch dates, I feel my heart touched by her warmth and love, and her true Hathor form seems to shimmer through.

She communicates directly with my mind in words that I can easily understand, "I have taken on this human disguise to help you be at ease and to insure that no passersby will be alarmed. You may call me Astarte."

"Today's lesson is to learn to use your heart, breath and body awareness to experience and amplify the Ka, or energy body. Daily practice will help you master these skills which underlie all further teachings and will also bring you peace and clarity of mind."

"Thank you Astarte. I will do my best. May I hold my special stones? They seem to help me understand and remember."

"Yes, my dear. That is a good idea. Please start with just your turquoise for the first exercise. It will help you to perceive your Ka body. Place it in your left hand where you may easily feel its energy. Now let us tone the A-U-M sound together to activate the energy and ready ourselves."

Imitating my teacher, I tale a deep breath as I close my eyes and chant with her. We tone this unfamiliar A-U-M three times. By the third time my voice comes into full resonance with hers and I feel myself begin to sink into an inner awareness. I smile as I notice my turquoise tingling in my hand.

"Good Niantha. You can feel the stone's energy. Allow it to soak into your hand. Then breathe it up your arm and into your body. Tell me what you notice."

"It seems to fill my whole body. I can feel my whole self at once from the inside.

"Perfect. Breathe in more energy from your turquoise and, as you exhale, allow your perception to continue to expand outward into the area that surrounds your physical body. This is your energy body or Ka. Can you sense it?"

"Yes! I am so much bigger than I thought."

"Now bring your attention to where your sit bones and your tailbone meet the earth. In the center of that triangle is an energetic opening from which you can send an energetic root deep into the earth.

I enjoy the sensation of my "root" moving down through the layers of the earth—sand, sandstone, rock. Gradually feeling warmer and warmer until finally penetrating the molten core.

"Good. Now breathe energy from the earth through that opening into your central channel that extends up through your whole body just in front of your spine. Breathe it all the way up to the crown of your head. Take a few more deep breaths, pulling more earth energy up into your central column and filling it as you exhale. Can you feel it?"

"Yes, I feel very rooted and the earth is flowing her nurturing energy into me. My central tube feels distinctly present, strong and balanced."

"I am so glad that you can feel this Niantha. For some it is not easy. Now shift your attention to the energetic opening at the top of your central channel at the crown of your head. Feel the warmth and light of the sun and the stars awaken your crown as the celestial energy moves into your central energy tube."

I feel a distinctive tingling and opening sensation at the top of my head. Instinctively I take a deep breath. With the exhale, I relax with pleasure as warmth and light flow in.

"Yes Niantha, breathe the light in, completely filling your central channel and making it glow."

"Now breathe both Earth Energy and Celestial Light into your central channel. And as you exhale, allow the energy and light to move out to fill your physical body. Continue to breathe, filling your central channel and your whole body and gradually moving further out to fill your Ka body which surrounds and interpenetrates your physical body."

"Let's take a few moments to practice this skill of feeding our Ka together."

"Remember to sit or stand in a relaxed but upright position. You may close your eyes if it helps you to focus. Connect with your central channel and the openings at the base and crown."

"Then let's breathe Ka for several rounds:

"Breathe earth energy up through the root. Exhale as it fills the central tube."

"Then breathe celestial light down through the crown and lighting up the tube."

"Exhale allowing the energy from the central channel to flow into your physical body and when you are ready into your Ka body as well."

"Repeat."

Although it takes some concentration to focus on breathing energy in this way, it seems to get easier and more natural with each repetition. I am feeling more and more alive and consciously aware of myself yet very peaceful. When Astarte signals for us to stop and I open my eyes, the whole world seems brighter, every detail sharper! I can tell that she knows what I am perceiving and is pleased with my progress.

"You are doing very well Niantha. There is one more important piece we must add---the heart! Then you will have a complete meditation practice that can be used daily to strengthen your Ka and expand your consciousness.

As Astarte says heart, I immediately feel my heart light up with the blissful expansive love I feel for my Heru! I know just the stone to use for this exercise and hold up my small falcon crystal. She beams her approval.

"For you, Niantha, I believe focusing on the heart center, which is located in the center of the chest just in front of your central channel, and bringing into awareness the feeling of unconditional love will not be a challenge. However, I want you to hold this loving heart presence as an accompaniment, to the breathing exercise you just learned. This will greatly increase the development of your Ka as well as your health and wellbeing. This meditation practice is not a time to lose yourself in dreaming about your beloved."

"Perhaps, you could try holding the turquoise in one hand and the crystal falcon in the other to help you maintain connection with both your body and your heart. In essence you are taking time each day to lovingly accept energy from the earth and the stars and feed it consciously with love and gratitude to your physical body and Ka body. The heart center is very important in this process not only because it holds the quality of love, but also because in humans it is the controller of the flow of breath and Ka."

"Do you understand?"

"Yes, I think I do. Thank you so much dear Astarte for sharing this beautiful wisdom. I promise I will practice every day."

NIANTHA – DESERT SANDSTORM

I have been practicing my Hathor meditation every morning upon waking and every evening before I sleep. It is both soothing and energizing. More and more I am experiencing my heart not just as the place of my feelings, but as the most important organ of my physical and Ka body and that I can use it as an instrument both receptively and expressively, to perceive as well as to act. Because it is the seat of my soul as well as the regulator of my life energy, to be consciously centered in my heart gives me access to my own holiness and to the holy nature of all life. Every detail of existence opens into the miracle of its divine nature. And all seems possible.

I know I must prepare to visit my beloved Horus in his heavenly Hathor home. And that somehow this will help me to fulfill my destiny. But how will this happen?

Those are the thoughts I am pondering as I walk through the rocky hills and dry sandy valleys between. I'm not meant to be out here alone, but my dear Shanti had to return with her brother to Dendera to visit their ailing mother. They have already been gone for 7 days. The beautiful day beckoned so sweetly—birds twittering and fresh gentle breezes tinkling the beaded door hanging—that I couldn't resist. I feel sure I now know the area surrounding our isolated little hut well enough to set out on my own for a much needed walk.

This land is so different from the lush green of the planted fields and fruit trees along the Nile near my home in Dendera. My eyes are drawn to the wide palette of color variations in the mineral rich rock formations from white to yellow to brown to red to purple to black. I smile at the surprise of bright wild flowers open in tiny clusters wherever morning dew has found an indentation in which to pool. There are even blooming azaleas though small and scraggly in this environment. And somehow the mysterious scent of some unfamiliar sweet incense comes and goes.

I am so enjoying the connection to the earth through my sandals and the feel of her energy moving up through my legs into my central channel, my heart and my body. The sun is warm and pleasant, not hot, and air soft and fresh as I breathe the light and celestial energy into my heart and Ka then back out through me in gratitude. My loneliness and restlessness have dissolved into a state of wonder and my heart is open wide in loving communion with all that is.

I shiver and notice the sun has shifted to the west and is partly hidden behind the clouds clinging to the top of the mountains.

"How long have I been walking? I must have lost track of time."

I turn to head back. I am sure I will be able to find my way home easily as I have been following this one trail the whole walk.

Just as my legs are beginning to feel a little weary, I notice that the wind has picked up—whistling through the rocky crevices and carrying tiny particles of sand that sting my skin. I am ill prepared. I ran outside without even a headscarf to wrap around me. I hurry my steps, but I am no longer sure I will make it to the hut before the sandstorm begins in earnest. I start to run, but as I breathe harder, I can feel the sand getting into my nose and mouth. It's getting difficult to see. I must slow down or lose the path if I haven't already. The wind is howling now and fear is churning in my stomach. It's too late! I must find shelter now!

I am completely blinded in the swirling sand, and I can barely breathe. I start to scream for help in sheer terror. But clamp my own hand over my mouth as sand rushes in, telling myself sternly, "This is no time to panic!"

I reach inside for my sacred heart and the energetic channel at my core, my rod of strength, and allow it to ground me into the earth. Immediately, I feel calmer, more present. I know that I must work with the elements and they will help me be safe. I turn until I feel the wind most strongly at my back. Now I can breathe more easily and at least see my hands and feet in front of me. I move forward slowly and carefully, trusting my hands and feet to guide me and keeping the wind at my back.

As I get more comfortable with this way of navigating, I find it's easier if I actually close my eyes and let my inner vision and senses take over. I notice that not only are my hands and feet finding their way but that they are aware of little nudges from the earth pushing them slightly this way or that. I feel my heart sending out pulses of love and listening for resonating responses that also guide my slow progress.

My heart is beginning to smile in recognition and I am not surprised when my hand touches a very large solid rock still warm from the sun. It is perfectly shaped and situated for me to sit in its lee and be well protected from the sand and the wind.

I settle in against the sheltering rock, getting as comfortable as I can, to wait out the storm. As I begin to relax, I notice how loudly the wind is still howling, with long almost melodious vowel sounds. I am moved to join in. Certainly no one will hear.

I take a deep breath and let my voice sing out "Ooooooh! Oooooooooh!" rising and falling with the wind song.

I feel all the tension and fear draining out of my body. I thank the wind for teaching me her song and helping me to heal this trauma with sound.

What other emotional wounds might I heal in this way? Immediately the memory arises of lying in bed at night as a small child desperately wanting and missing my mother. And I feel how I hold that sad lonely abandoned feeling in my jaw and my throat. I knew that she had died. Calling out to her or crying would do no good and make my father angry. So I clamped my mouth tightly shut and felt my jaw and throat ache with the pain of her loss.

Now as I sink into that remembered pain, I allow myself to feel it and breathe with it, waiting for the sounds to emerge.

At first soft and tentative and gradually louder, "Maaaah, maaaaaaaaahhh, mmmmaaaaaaaahhhhh!"

Then guttural wrenching sobbing sounds. I continue to wail until the expression of the emotion quiets and completes of its own will.

As I breathe in the peacefulness through my whole being, I become aware of my mother's loving presence in my heart, as both her earthly self and her goddess self, always there to hold me and to guide me.

"And what is my sound dear one?"

From my smiling open heart, I tone with slow sure resonance, "Ma__ ma, ma__ ma".

Then I slide down into sleep feeling held in her warm loving embrace.

I awake to silence as the morning sun touches my face. I am aware of a presence nearby and turn my head to see my Hathor teacher Astarte smiling at me. I quickly stand, smoothing my hair and dress, and bow to her in greeting.

"Let us sit my child. It is time for your next lesson. But first let us refresh ourselves. I brought nuts and dates and water."

"Thank you. You are truly a gift from heaven dear Astarte!"

I discretely rinse my mouth and hands before drinking thirstily. And taste every bite with gratitude.

When our breakfast is complete, we naturally sit in silent meditation for some time. To conclude I join Astarte in toning "A-U-M"

"Niantha, you have been diligent in your practice and mastered the Ka meditation I gave you. I am very pleased at how well you handled the challenging initiation of the dust storm. I believe you learned a great deal about your emotional body and sound in the process. Is that not so?"

"Oh yes! It was amazing to discover how and where my experienced feelings vibrate in my body and to discover the corresponding sounds."

"But most of all, I am so grateful for your training to move into my central column and ground it into the earth. If not for that, I think my overwhelming fear would have made me completely senseless and I could have been lost and buried in the blowing sand."

"The emotional body and the Ka body are closely linked and understanding their connection and how to use it with awareness to master this unique human gift of emotions is key to ascending from the earth-bound state to a more heavenly level of consciousness beyond time and space. The key is allowing oneself to be aware of feelings and emotional responses to situations so that they can be noticed and balanced. By strengthening the Ka and by bringing the emotions into full and positive awareness, a person can greatly accelerate his or her evolution."

"As you experienced, a full-fledged attack of fear can override the mental body and you won't be able to think, but rather will be paralyzed with fear. Moving your awareness into the Ka can transmute the fear very quickly!"

"When you experience an intense, difficult emotion or feeling, first identify where in the body it's located because you will need that reference point. Then you go to the Ka, by shifting and holding your awareness in the central column, the energetic tube that goes right through the middle of the body. This allows the emotional body to begin to shift. As the vibration of fear begins to oscillate with the stability of the central column, the fear will become more subtle, more manageable."

"Thank you for explaining, dear Astarte. I don't think I will ever forget this lesson! Can you tell me more about the role of sound in mastering emotions?"

"Not only can we learn to be aware of how and where each emotion vibrates in our physical body, but we can discover its sound signature."

"Emotions can be viewed much like musical chords, some of which are melodic and soothing while others are grating and cacophonous. Children let themselves spontaneously express what they are feeling through crying, laughing, yelling, or some other sound until they have been told that they cannot do this and must be quiet. But the natural biological impulse is to make a sound in response to an especially strong emotion. The suppression of emotion is not healthy. So I want to encourage you to continue to be aware of emotions as you experience them and in recall and to use your voice to find and express their sounds."

"Simply allow your awareness to move into the area of the body where the emotion resides. Then take a deep breath allowing yourself to make the sound of the emotion as you exhale. Keep making the sound until you feel relieved and clear."

"Yes, that is exactly what I experienced. I am excited to continue practicing this to release discordant emotional energy. But how is this related to the beautiful singing/toning that I'm learning from my beloved Horus?"

"Ah, that is another wonderful aspect of expressing sound! Sound can also be used to access specific states of consciousness, including states of bliss, healing, love, peace. When you find yourself in a desirable state, allow your awareness to move into the feeling of that state fully. Then permit a sound or series of sounds to emerge. Listen to the sounds you voice. They are a reflection of its sound signature and will allow you to access that state again."

"When you listen to and/or join others toning or singing in expression of a particular state of consciousness, you will find yourself moving into resonance with their sounds and their state of consciousness. What a beautiful way to experience the loving union between beloveds! Within the sound of your voice are the keys to innumerable worlds."

"Niantha, it is time for us to journey back to your little house. Shanti has returned home and is wondering where you are. Please continue to practice your meditation daily as well as these new skills with feelings and sounds. As you clear and balance your emotional body, build your Ka, and master using sound to access higher states of consciousness, you will be preparing yourself for your next initiation."

"I promise I will practice faithfully. Thank you for all your help and wisdom dear Astarte."

SOPHIA – IN NEED OF HEALING

It's dark and stuffy in here and I can't breathe. My head aches and my throat is so so sore! I can't even imagine being able to sleep scrunched into this little curtained bunk aboard the night train from Luxor to Cairo. I can't believe I'm getting sick. What a bummer! But I suppose maybe not so surprising after all the amazing energy work over the last several days.

As the light of morning begins to seep into the compartment, I'm beginning to cough uncontrollably—each hack like a knife in my chest. I struggle back into my clothes and prepare to get off the train and locate my luggage. The air is smoky and dusty and I wrap my head and cover my face with a scarf.

Somehow I manage to get myself and my belongings onto the bus and sit in mute misery as we head to the Mina Oberoy in Cairo. I'm barely aware of the grand beauty of this 19th Century Turkish Hotel as I check in and head for my room. Grateful that our rooms have all the modern conveniences, I sink into my bed and succumb to a full-blown case of bronchitis.

I try to smile as my roommate comes in full of excitement about the day's plans. We have one free day before we visit the Great Pyramid at Giza. She's telling me about the plan to visit the famous Cairo Market and the ancient Coptic Church.

"Go on without me I," I croak out.

I would love to go, but I know it's impossible. I don't have the energy to get up and get ready. I just hope if I allow myself to rest and heal today, I'll be able to fully experience the Great Pyramid tomorrow.

Although I still feel exhausted, I can't seem to sleep. I keep coughing and my head and chest ache. I feel so sad and separate from everyone—ready to cry. I have worked so hard over the last couple years to clear a lifetime of chronic issues with respiratory allergies, asthma and bronchitis, seeking help from homeopaths, psychics and psychologists. I thought I had made such good progress, and now here I am having a healing crisis alone in Egypt of all places!

"So what is this about?" I ask my little girl inside.

Little Sophie pours out her pain. "Oh I feel like my little girl self----trying to breathe carefully to keep from coughing. I want out. I want out. I want out!" I sob.

"Not this again! Everybody else is working/playing with all this esoteric cool stuff, and I'm stuck just being my dumb old little girl self who can't even run and play 'cause I'll wheeze."

I find myself longing to be held in the loving healing energy I experienced in Luxor with Isis and the Hathors. That felt so familiar and right. Where are they now? And what about Niantha?

"Please come to me! Please help me!"

And then, somehow there she is -- the beautiful Egyptian princess – floating above me in her energy body with ephemeral Hathor figures hovering nearby.

"Dear Sophie, know that you are one of us. We did not abandon you in the Earth realm. We are still here and ready to come when you call."

Niantha moves my hands on my body and uses them to flow her love into my heart and hips to ground and calm me. She encourages me to breathe deeply and fully. Then she touches my third eye and I find myself slipping into a vision she is sharing of herself—scared and lost in the desert sandstorm until she discovers how to not only save herself but release old childhood trauma using sound and the natural elements.

The vision fades but the presence of Niantha and the Hathors is still very strong.

"Now it is your turn Sophie. Where do you hold this old story of illness, asthma, being alone and separate? Place your hands there."

I am surprised to find myself placing my hands on my throat. Even though I would have expected it to be my belly, where I always feel difficult emotions like fear and anger, or my aching lungs, I know that my throat is absolutely the right place to focus. Memories surface of being singled out as the one who can't sing, can't carry a tune, and of being told to be quiet and stop arguing and complaining. And even earlier going to the hospital at a very young age to have my tonsils removed.

"Now take a deep breath and let whatever sound wants to emerge come out."

At first, my voice sounds strained and strangled, ending in a fit of coughing, but then I take another deep breath and begin howling out all my pain and frustration—louder and louder. It feels so good.

As the feeling of release is complete, I naturally and spontaneously transition to a more melodious and joyful toning and am joined by Niantha and the Hathors. My heart swells with the feeling of connectedness and bliss.

NIANTHA – JOURNEY TO SIRIUS

I feel sad. I've learned so much, but still I feel separate from my beloved Horus. There is something more I must learn. I remember that Astarte promised me another initiation. I think the time is now. I am restless like just before my sandstorm experience. I sense that there is a big journey ahead. But I don't know how to start.

This morning in my meditation, it felt as if my very soul wanted to escape from my body and this place, wanted to fly free. Oh dear Hathors, can sound help me do this? In my heart I hear a whispered "yes!"

"This time dear Niantha, you must be very conscious and deliberately use all the skills you have learned. Our loving guidance is always available. But it is now time for you to come to us—to our world, and the inter-dimensional shift that is necessary must be completely of your own free will."

As I contemplate this message, I begin to feel a rising of confidence to match my longing and urgency. It is time to journey to my beloved's home in the stars, and I know the perfect time and place from which to start. Tomorrow night at the full dark of the moon when the star world will be most visible I must return to the little cave up the mountain near our small hut where I first met Astarte and where I last embraced my Heru. I must prepare myself and Shanti for this journey so that she will not be worried if I don't return.

45

As the sun is setting, I slowly walk up the hill to my meditation cave. I feel mentally and physically prepared as I place the food, water, scarves and blankets that I have brought inside. I take a seat on the rock outcropping in front of the cave, breathe deeply and slowly, send my grounding cord into the earth and begin my Ka meditation. As I watch the stars winking on, I feel my heart open in awe and loving connection with the celestial light. I wait, sitting in sweet peaceful stillness and communion. If I notice I am drifting off, I return to actively engaging in my Ka breathing practice. It feels important to be relaxed but also fully conscious, alert to choose wisely how I use my attention.

It is full night now. The sky is filled with innumerable stars and the cool night air drifts with the wafting scent of the acacias. My gaze is drawn to the area of the sky where the star Sirius is shining brightly. A smile plays across my lips as I begin to hear feint whispers of the Hathor singing that I learned from my beloved Horus, and I feel a tugging at my heart and womb. He is calling me. Will I truly be able to go to him this time?

I want to make sure that nothing is holding me back. I stand and place my hands and my awareness fully on my body and my energy field. Moving up one chakra at a time, I connect with each area, using vocal toning to release any fear or unease. Feeling clear open ready, I reach my arms upwards, ready to fly to my love. The beautiful wordless singing is louder now and I join in with delight. It is time for my long-awaited journey!

"First make your body safe," cautions an inner voice.

I move into the cave and lay down wrapped in my blankets. My body feels warm and comfortable. I relax and allow myself to return to my meditative state and fully engage with the sound of our vocal communion. I know with certainty that all I have to do is trust and allow my soul to fall up out of my body and Horus will catch me. My awareness is no longer in my body, but I can see my body resting safely below me. I can sense that I am securely corded to my body and will be able to return with ease.

"Good my love. Now look at me."

"Oh my Heru!" And I fall into his arms. Such bliss!

In this now, I experience myself to be tall and beautiful, a perfect match for my beloved Horus. Somehow I can hear, understand, and speak the light language that he and his family use. I delight in moving about and exploring their crystalline homes and temples. When Heru and I move and dance together, we become spheres of light then shift into more substantial but diaphanous bodies when we are still.

"Come my Hatti! I want to introduce you to my family. We have all been waiting for this moment when you would be ready to come be with us in our home here on our Sirian planet."

Soon I am surrounded by smiling Hathors, welcoming me in their buzzing light language, and touching my heart somehow directly with their hearts in unconditional love and acceptance. I feel more at home than I have ever felt before.

Then everyone fades away and I am left with the most beautiful woman I have ever seen. She emanates motherly love and caring and her eyes shine with the most amazing light. Somehow there is a familiar scent of lotus flowers wafting gently about her. This takes me back instantly to my earliest memories.

"Mama!" I cry with tears running down my cheeks.

"Come my daughter. I have so much to share with you"

As She guides me through a beautiful crystal temple space into her private chamber, the Hathor singing becomes all encompassing. I realize that -- *these sounds clean and feed the Ka body and bring it in clear resonance with the human heart and by extension with the whole physical body creating a field of healing and well-being. As this base is strengthened and cleared, there is enough available attention and relaxed awareness to open the inter-dimensional portal for soul travel. She doesn't have to explain this, I know it as I experienced it, witnessed it.*

But then I begin to experience what her unconditionally loving presence makes possible as I shake and cry, releasing every bit of stored pain and grief. And then I understand that this healing process is only the beginning, the readying for all the lessons she has to teach me. I glimpse the future in which she will impart all her womanly and motherly wisdom of sexuality, pregnancy, childbirth, child-raising as well as her spiritual wisdom that make her the Goddess Hator.

"Come my child it is time to prepare for your wedding."

I gasp in surprise.

"Don't worry my dear we will teach you everything you need to know about lovemaking and you will please your Horus greatly! Sexual union is so much more than making babies and momentary pleasure."

NIANTHA
PREPARING FOR ECSTATIC UNION

I awaken in a small crystalline room, not sure how I got there. Did I faint? I am lying on a soft bed feeling relaxed and sleepy, and I am naked! I'm just about to panic when I notice my beloved teacher Astarte sitting close by and smiling at me. But she no longer appears as an old crone but is now lithe and beautiful in her luminous light body.

"All is well dear one. I am here to help you learn about the powers of your woman's body and how to stimulate, enjoy and use your sexual energy to feed your Ka body. This will prepare you for ecstatic union with your beloved Horus. "

"Niantha, please know that I will be here with you to guide you through this initiation into sex magic and will insure that we are not interrupted. It is essential that you feel completely relaxed and safe in order to fully experience, and later share, the power and beauty of your divine woman self. I will demonstrate and direct but only your own hands will touch you."

"To begin, please place your hands on your hips, allowing your awareness to settle there fully."

I feel a sense of heavy solid presence there in my hips, in the base of my spine and extending down my legs into my feet. My whole body seems more present and I feel the familiar experience of my grounding cord rooting downwards----down, down, down----finally connecting me to my physical body still resting peacefully in the mountain cave.

"Yes, my dear, your soul and Ka body are still well-connected to your physical body which is safely sleeping. Very little time will pass on earth while you are busy here."

"You have already mastered filling your Djed or central channel with Earth and Celestial energy and using that energy to feed your Ka. Now you will experience the seven seals or energy plexuses located along the Djed and begin to practice raising your own serpent like energy up through these seals in order to create an expanded state of being."

"Return your focus to your hands on your hips. The first seal is located at the base of the central channel at the center of the triangle created by your two sit-bones and your pelvis. Moving your hands forward so that your fingers rest on your pelvic bone will help you to feel the area of the first seal. Take your time getting comfortable with focusing here and see what you notice."

My inner vision is filled with red and golden light and a pulsing energy. The energy wants strongly to move upwards. At the same time I am aware of erotic sensations in my vulva and my breasts and nipples. Focusing on the arousal sensations seems to strengthen and brighten the red and golden energy and the call for it to move upward.

"Very good. Allow the energy to vibrate up your Djed into the second seal, which is in your womb area below the navel. You can place your hands on your low belly to help focus your awareness."

There is a sensation of pulling or calling down and inward and the image of the whirlpool effect of water draining. The colors and energy are more muted as in moonlight. I also feel like my hands are resting on my pregnant belly. The impulse to move upward is softer and more patient.

"Move your hands so they are resting on your upper belly just below your breasts where your ribs meet. Allow the energy and your focus to move up into this third seal."

I am not as comfortable here. There are anxious thoughts about this whole experience and a desire to jump up and do something. As I breathe and gradually feel the area become very warm, I relax. There is a sensation of almost movement and coming into alignment with my womb and heart. And the energy in my 3rd seal spills naturally through the open passageway into my heart.

"Ahhh! And now you are in the 4th seal at your heart. Go ahead and move your hands there and allow yourself to be fully present in your heart."

I find myself taking deep slow breaths and there is a sensation of floating peacefully on gently rolling waves of warm water. I am shimmering with the light of love. I feel connection with my Goddess mother and my beloved Horus and some wistful missing of my little brother. I feel wonderfully held in my expansive heart but also very aware of my whole central column and my whole body and Ka body especially my feet, my womb and breasts. It is hard to imagine moving on from this relaxed and blissful state.

"Slowly glide your hands upward, drawing along the light and love filled watery energy, to embrace your throat."

Oh my, I feel so tall! Like a Hathor! There is a ringing in my ears reminding me of the Hathor singing and a desire to open my mouth and join in. And the growing upward pull is so strong that I feel I could fly.

Slide your hands up along the sides of your face then back together to meet cupping your eyes."

It is very dark and my vision is turned inward. All my other senses seemed turned off.

"Yes, focus down and in. What do you see?"

In the middle of my head, behind my brow there is a small golden bowl. There is a sense of waiting stillness. My inner vision draws upward to see an exquisite pearl-like droplet ready to fall. My inner vision brightens and I see that the droplet is emerging from the mouth of a serpent and a second serpent is facing the first. She has a liquid ruby droplet hanging from her fang. I am aware of the strong pulsing writhing energy that has powered their sinuous climb up my central column but I am held in breathless anticipation by the steady infinite loving stillness in their twin gaze.

And then, in slow motion, the droplets float down into the bowl----the ruby and pearl drops spreading and dissolving into each other! I taste an indescribable sweetness in the back of my throat as my vision disappears in an explosion of pure Light and waves of blissful sensation!

"Beautiful! Stay with your experience---fully receiving this ecstatic state. Allow it to expand outward to nourish your Ka body as well. Gradually the energy will dissipate and you will fall asleep. You are completely safe and no one will disturb you. I will return when you are fully rested."

NIANTHA – QUEEN OF DENDERA

Stretching and yawning, I come slowly awake, surprised to feel the hard rock of the cave floor below my blanket instead of the soft comfort of my bed in the crystalline chamber.

"What?" I exclaim as my eyes pop open.

What a disappointment to find myself back in my body in the cave.

"What about our wedding?"

As if from a great distance away, I hear Astarte's voice. "Soon, but not quite as soon as we thought. First your Earth body and Earth family need your attention. "

"Niantha, it's an emergency! I brought someone to see you." I recognize Shanti's urgent call coming from the cave entrance.

Quickly I make myself presentable and go out.

What a surprise to see my younger brother standing there with Shanti.

"Geo!" I cry and wrap him in a tight hug.

"Oh Hatti, our father is very ill! We must hurry if you are to see him before he dies."

Shanti and Geo and I hurry back to Dendera with no effort to be secretive. When I enter my father's room, it is clear that he is barely hanging on, waiting for me to arrive.

As I bend to kiss his cheek, he grasps me to him and whispers in my ear. "Niantha, I am so sorry. Your mother told me just before she died that there were special plans for you, and that she would see to your eventual marriage to the sky god of your destiny. But I didn't listen. And now it is too late. King Bagra is determined to have you as promised and to add our prosperous kingdom to his own. Even now he is waiting just outside the city with armed forces for news of my death."

With his last strength, King Theron sits up and removes the sacred jeweled chain he once received from his own father from around his neck and puts it over my bowed head. I feel its weight settle on my shoulders and chest.

"I proclaim my daughter Niantha Queen of Dendera."

His body sinks back down, his eyes close and his breath stops.

Tears streaming down my face, I throw myself on his still form.

"Oh father, I love you. All is forgiven. I will do my best to fulfill your will and that of my blessed mother."

SOPHIA – GIZA

Feeling much better, I arise early and head out in the Cairo sunshine to explore the beautiful gardens of the palatial Mina Oberoy Hotel before joining the others for breakfast. It's the last leg of our Sacred Egypt Journey. So much has happened. It's very hard to imagine returning home to my previous life. I feel that I have so much to integrate. Will I still have this strong connection with the Hathors and my dear Niantha when I return to America?

I can't help feeling sad even though this is meant to be an exciting culmination of our journey as we head to the Great Pyramid and the Sphinx today. My feet guide me to a secluded alcove surrounded by flowering hibiscus with a fountain and bench in the middle. I sit to meditate, aware of both church bells and the singing of the Muslim call to prayer in the distance. As I sink inwards the sound becomes the now familiar Hathor singing.

"Are you calling me?"

"Come Sophia Rose. You are one of us. Fly on our voices. We will never be far. We are permanently in your heart space, where there is a portal to access other dimensions."

It feels like I am floating through the vastness of space and stars. And at the same time I feel held lovingly in the sound of the Hathor voices.

"Thank you! I will always cherish these experiences. I will never forget you dear Hathors."

We board our buses and begin the short drive up the road to the site of the Giza Pyramid Complex. The sight that comes into view is breathtaking! There at the center is the unbelievably tall Great Pyramid and clustered around are two other large pyramids and several smaller ones. In front is the ancient Sphinx. These wonders of the world are very real and right in front of us! Our group will be the second to make the journey into the King's Chamber of the Great Pyramid. So I have time to wander and explore the complex a bit.

I find myself immediately attracted to the Sphinx. As I move closer, I can see where pieces have worn or broken off. I move across a raised walkway with chain link fencing on either side to get as close as possible. Below I can see where work is being done on the base of the Sphinx. Standing on the viewing platform, I can't really touch the huge stone structure but the energy is quite palpable and I feel a visceral tug to enter.

I stand as much off to the side as I can and lightly close my eyes, allowing myself to be pulled down and forward meditatively to stand between the long paws of the Sphinx. I am facing huge carved doors in her chest. I place my hands on my heart and wish for Hathor accompaniment. I feel their presence and a background hum of voices. The doors swing open on their own, and I slowly walk in. I feel a touch of terror as the doors shut behind me.

Then I notice a loud purring and glowing in the dimness are huge cat eyes. Oh my! It's a huge lioness—Sekhmet? Even though she is immense and could easily crush me in her huge jaws in one bite, I somehow know that she loves me very much and that I must trust her. I move closer and she gently lays me down between her paws. I can feel her warm breath and her rough and surprisingly dry tongue caressing me all over.

The feeling is incredibly tender and heart opening. Tears leak silently from my eyes and I know that I am being gifted with a very deep healing. When she stops, I rise and press my body and face into her fur. I inhale her clean animal scent and listen to her rumbling purr, ---whispering "I love you. I love you. Thank you. Thank you."

"Come Sophia. You have an appointment to keep." My Hathor guides are nudging me to move on.

SOPHIA – APPOINTMENT WITH FATE

Although I'm not sure where I am going, the way just keeps opening up ahead of me as I am rushed through interior passageways. Finally I am back out on the Giza Plateau facing the Great Pyramid. But it feels different—a different time or dimension. There are no tourists and there are a series of carved archways rising between me and the pyramid. It reminds me of the 12 Gates at the Karnak Temple in Luxor. I hurry through. Somehow I am not surprised to see Isis waiting for me when I pass through the final gate. But who is that with her? Another Egyptian God—Thoth I think. And Charlie—one of my new friends from the tour bus!

"Charlie! Is that really you? What are you doing here?"

"Sophie! I was about to ask you the same thing" Charlie chuckles.

It has to be him. I would recognize that jolly laugh anywhere!

Before we can continue our conversation, Thoth and Isis announce in a serious resonant tone, "We have brought you both here to teach you how to create a sacred Column of Light connecting the heart of our planet Earth with the Light of the Cosmos. This will be an important aspect of your life and journeys together as Lightworkers in the days and years ahead."

They motion for us to step closer together and ask us to join hands. Immediately I am aware of a magnetic connection between us as well as a powerful magnetic pull through my feet down into the Earth. I also feel a strong sensation of tingling and opening in my crown. Then there is a beautiful brightness of light from above pouring through the circle of our joined hands into this sacred spot on the Earth. Both Charlie and I shiver as this immense energy runs through us. My ears are filled with a sound of joyful Hathor singing.

We both open our eyes and smile in surprise and delight! The pyramid has become a diaphanous glow of crystalline light! The crystals appear to be growing and taking on form in front of our eyes. The sound of the Hathor singing is very vibrant and compelling and we find ourselves joining in. Our voices are blending, separating, blending with theirs and each other. I feel so joyful and alive—like I am falling in love!

As the sound crescendos and begins to soften and hold steady, the crystals complete their dance of growth and settle into the shape of a giant pyramid of light. *The geometry amplifies the ability of the crystals to hold the sound. And the sound helps the crystals to create the geometry.*

"So that's how the great pyramids at Giza were created!" exclaims Charlie in awe. And I feel a sense of affirmation.

SOPHIA
KING'S CHAMBER OF THE
GREAT PYRAMID

It is quiet now and the light has faded. We are standing in front of the Great Pyramid in the same impressive, but worn, condition as it first appeared when our bus arrived on the Giza Plateau. It's time to join the rest of our group, which is now lining up to enter.

There are about 60 of us. The air is tense with both anticipation and some dread. We have been told that the passageway leading to the King's Chamber is steep, dark, and tight. We enter one at a time, silently passing the guards, and follow each other up the slanting wooden walkway through the tunnel carved in the stone. There are lights along the floor every so often, making it less dark than I expected. Although I have to duck my head just a bit, there is plenty of room for us to walk easily single file. I take slow measured breaths and feel calm and grounded, opening my awareness to the coming experience. I am enjoying the quiet sense of passing through a sacred portal.

Eventually, I enter the King's Chamber. I am rather taken aback by how large and well lit it is. There is plenty of room for all of us and we sit around the edges against the stone walls, leaving a large open space in the middle with a stone sarcophagus towards one end. I am craving dark and silence, imagining this as a place of death-like initiation for Egyptian mystery adepts hundreds of years ago.

The leader of our group seems intent upon creating a group connection and ceremony. He and several others speak briefly, giving messages from their guides. One of the men has brought along a crystal bowl and is asked to play it. At first I am very interested to experience what atmosphere will be created by the sound in this sacred chamber. Will my beloved Hathors come and "sing" with us?

But as the high-pitched sounds ring on and on, I am becoming very uncomfortable and on edge. It feels off! A weird energy hovers around us, maybe even non-human entities. What is he calling in? Certainly not the Hathors! I instinctively feel my grounding cord going down through the pyramid into the earth and breathe calming earth energy into my central channel. I open my eyes and notice that there are others who are feeling uncomfortable. Some have their hands over their ears. A few of my new friends from the bus are glancing around and pointing at something in the air with their chins.

Maybe they are seeing the presence that I am feeling. Finally, the sounding of the crystal bowl stops, and our leader asks us all to stand and join hands as we chant the AUM. I rise feeling queasy.

"Please help us," I cry silently. "Niantha, help me call in the Hathors!"

I keep my intent to connect with the Hathors strong, as I take a deep breath and join the others in toning AUM, letting my voice be strong and resonant. I start to feel more grounded, calm and heart-centered and our circle becomes noticeably more cohesive.

I can feel them, the Hathors, joining our circle. Hands on the back of each of our hearts. And singing with us. We are warming and relaxing letting go. A buzzing sound grows and a feeling of being cleared energetically. Then there is profound stillness and peace. As the singing starts again, it seems very celestial with a down pouring of divine light filling our hearts and bodies. We are reminded to stay grounded and allow ourselves to be a channel for healing light to enter the heart of the Earth.

As the music stops, I look around at everyone's shining faces and light-filled energy bodies and see that although we are still standing in the King's Chamber, we are also simultaneously in the crystalline pyramid temple on Sirius where the portal is to the original home of the Hathors in another dimensional universe. Amazing! Thank you Hathors.

SOPHIA – CHARLIE

After the amazing and powerful experiences of today, I have no energy to interact with anyone. I sit in silence on the bus with my eyes closed grounding and trying to digest. Then I head straight for my room at the hotel and flop on my bed.

I awake a couple hours later to the sound of the phone. "Hello," I mumble.

"Sophie, this is Charlie. Uh…how are you?" He sounds nervous.

"Oh Charlie, I don't know…" I trail off.

"We need to talk."

"We sure do!" I feel heat rising in my throat and face at the thought.

"Shall we meet for dinner?"

"I guess, but I sure don't want to talk in front of everyone else. Maybe we could go for a walk afterwards?"

"Ok. Shall we meet at the hotel restaurant in 20 minutes?"

Sure."

Suddenly, I feel wide awake and jump up to take a quick shower and dress in fresh clothes---well the freshest I have left in my bag! This reminds me that I need to repack. The flight back to the U.S. is tomorrow night!

It's a pretty raucous gathering at dinner as it's the last night we'll all be together. Charlie is quite well known and liked among these folks. He's giving and receiving lots of hugs and laughing and discussing future plans.

I'm quiet and force myself to smile pleasantly and try to enjoy the wide array of salads and vegies available from the buffet. However, when I feel that I've eaten as much as I can and get up to leave, Charlie gets right up and follows me out. No one even seems to notice.

Outside the air is balmy and fragrant with flowers. The grounds are lit just enough to make walking the paths easy. I don't think either of us knows where to start the conversation.

Finally, Charlie says, "I saw them, you know, the Hathors, come swarming around you and then all of us in the King's Chamber. Did you call them? I must say I was really relieved. There were some very nasty reptilian E.T.'s in there with us and they were beginning to invade some of our energy bodies. But the Hathors seemed to have no problem shifting the energy and sending them away."

"Wow, Charlie! You actually saw them! I did call the Hathors. I didn't know what else to do. The energy from the crystal bowl playing felt so bad!"

"Sophie, I think the Hathors would tell you to trust your feelings. In this case, they affirmed what you felt and what I saw. They told me it is important to be aware that there are many beings hanging about our planet who are not spiritually evolved, rather they are more like energy vampires. They stressed that sound is very powerful and like any vibrational energy can be used for good or evil purposes. Look what happened with Atlantis for example. So it is important for energy workers to be well-grounded, heart–centered channels of light and to be fully present with clear benevolent intent."

"Yes, that's the message I got as well. Isn't the Hathor singing blissful? Did you also have a vision of the King's Chamber becoming the crystalline temple pyramid? Maybe the same one we saw earlier?"

"Oh! I sure did! Seeing that crystal pyramid and hearing that celestial singing and the Light! It's the most amazing, heart – opening experience I have ever had. And that brings up another reason we need to talk. I don't think we were brought into each other's visions by accident!"

By now, my whole body is zinging with excited energy. The connection between us is feeling very strong and magnetic again. "Will he kiss me?" I wonder.

By this time we have somehow found our way to the same secluded garden where I had meditated this morning. Was that really only just this morning? As Charlie draws me towards the bench, I think, "Ooh, this is it!"

But instead of the sweet embrace I'm expecting, I see Charlie looking at me seriously.

"I have a message for you Sophie. I was meditating this afternoon and a beautiful Egyptian-looking young woman came to me."

'Tell Sophie I need her help desperately. And you must help
  Sophie help me. Please, please help me!'"

"It must have been Princess Niantha—my dear dear Niantha! Oh
we must contact her immediately, and I think we know how!"

Without any more words, Charlie and I stand simultaneously and
join hands to create a portal of Light. Our position is just right for
us to be standing in a pool of moonlight. I feel energy circling
through our bodies and joined hands and our hearts opening
into resonance with each other. We look up in the direction of
Sirius, take a deep breath and begin to chant "AUM" together.

Our intent to contact the Hathors and Niantha is strong. As we
sink into a meditative state, we can hear the beautiful tones of
Hathor singing, impelling us to join in. Our Ka bodies are leaving
our physical bodies behind and lifting upwards, flying on the
music. Soon we are again in the crystal pyramid temple we
visited earlier today. This time in the home of the Hathors on
Sirius!

But standing in front of us is not Niantha, but Horus and his
Goddess Mother!

They communicate directly with our minds. "Thank you for
coming. We have brought you here together to help us create a
multi-dimensional portal between our Hathor star home and
your planet Earth. This will link us directly not only with Egypt
in the era in which Niantha lives but also in the time in which
you are currently living. By being a part of this process you will
not only help Niantha to marry Horus and live out her destiny to
bring our teachings to her people as the Goddess Hator, but also
you will be beginning an important new chapter of your own
lives both as a couple and as lightworkers helping to make our
teachings available to humanity at your momentous time in
history."

My mind boggles at the magnitude of what they are communicating, but my heart is jumping with excitement and a big Yes! I shyly peak at Charlie and see from his smile that he's feeling the same way.

I know he must be even more confused by the suddenness of all this than I, as he hasn't had all the experiences with Niantha and the Hathors that I have recently. Yet Charlie gives my hand a loving squeeze and says softly, "I'm in if you're in."

I squeeze his hand back and nod "yes" with a smile. So I guess we're a couple now? As crazy as this all seems, it also feels completely right!

SOPHIA
WEDDING OF NIANTHA AND HORUS

"But where is Niantha?" I say as we turn back to face our hosts.

"She returned to Dendera because her father was dying and Theron named her Queen with his last breath. She had been hiding away in the mountains to escape the arranged marriage with old King Bagra. She was also studying with her Hathor teacher and preparing for our marriage. "

"Now," continues Horus, "Niantha is trapped in the temple at Dendera. Bagra and his forces have the complex surrounded and are preparing for a forced wedding. She cannot escape this time because Bagra would declare her dead and himself as the rightful king."

As Horus describes Niantha's situation, her image and her presence become clearer and clearer until finally Charlie and I are standing with her in the temple at Dendera. All three of us in a large column of light!

"Oh, you have come! Thank you. Thank you."

Before we can even begin to explain how we got here, the most amazing celestial sound of Hathor singing is rising all around us and the crystalline light has expanded and brightened. We can't help but join in!

The overlapping of dimensions synchronizes more completely, and we are simultaneously in the temple at Dendera and in the Hathor temple on Sirius.

"Oh Horus! Mother!" cries Niantha.

The miraculous music and light has brought all the priestesses running. Soon the local citizenry, and even King Bagra and his men, are looking and pressing in.

While everyone is still frozen in awe, the Goddess Mother steps forward. Appearing in her tall diaphanous Hathor form, she draws Horus and Niantha to her. Joining their hands, she proclaims, "My son, my daughter, you are now husband and wife through all eternity. I bless your marriage."

She, then, removes her jeweled goddess headpiece and hands it to Horus, who tenderly places it on Niantha's head and kisses her third eye.

In that moment, with everyone witnessing, Niantha is transformed into her beautiful tall Hathor self and floats off with Horus to celebrate their marriage. It is certain that no one will doubt the union of this sky god and goddess and that there will be no usurping of the throne of Dendera. The cheering is loud and joyous and surely the feasting will begin shortly!

For Charlie and I, the scene is already fading as we feel ourselves being pulled back into our physical bodies in the garden of a Cairo Hotel in the year 2012.

And then, finally, the kiss! And what a kiss it is! A profound, heart resonating communication and affirmation of all that we just experienced together!

NIANTHA
BLISSFUL UNION WITH HORUS

"Queen Niantha and her god husband Horus have withdrawn to the most private inner suite of the palace at Dendera to finally consummate their love in physical union. " says a voice in my head.

I look around and sure enough I am standing with my Heru in the beautiful room my parents once shared.

I have been waiting for this moment for so long. My heart is beating fast. I am so happy and excited to finally be with my beloved, but I'm also nervous.

"Hatti, my queen, my goddess, my beloved, please let us relax together on the bed. We will go very slowly. Each touch will be tender and exquisite. Our love will guide us perfectly into a physical union of heavenly bliss."

I allow him to guide me gently down to lie beside him on the bed. Following Heru's lead, I take slow deep breaths and feel myself relax. We turn to face each other. As we look deeply into each other's eyes, I feel the magnetic pull between our souls and I know that my whole life has been preparing me for this moment. I relax even more and feel very present and aware inside my body.

I reach out to touch my Heru's face. My fingertips explore and caress its shape and linger on his lips. I want him to kiss me!

Our lips meet softly, gently, and then with greater and greater urgency. His taste is so sweet! The desire to touch to merge is very strong, and soon not only our mouths, but every part of us, is pressed deliciously skin to skin.

"Slowly, slowly Hatti beloved," moans Horus catching his breath. "Come, sit on my lap and we will meditate and breathe together."

We sit and adjust our positions so that I am facing him astride his legs. Our breaths deepen and slow, synchronizing with each other. I feel myself relaxing into a meditative state, my eyes closing.

Horus lightly grazes my nipples with his fingertips. My breasts tingle with pleasurable sensation and so does my vulva!

As he takes first one nipple then the other in his mouth gently licking and sucking, my pleasure mounts and I find myself beginning to sway and undulate slightly.

"Aaah," whispers Heru, "the serpents awaken."

And I remember my experience of the serpent energies that I discovered in my training with Astarte in the Hathor crystalline pyramid. Yes, the twin serpents are awake! I feel them at the base of my central channel, and I feel a sparkling of Light at my crown that is calling to them to twine their way upward.

"You are ready my love."

Heru moves me closer so that the velvety soft tip of his penis pushes gently into the wet opening of my labia. We settle back into a state of deep loving presence, taking time to be with what is happening within. I am aware of a subtle conversation beginning between the tip of his male member and the innermost depths of my vagina, my deepest female self, a calling to each other.

"Hatti." And my attention is drawn outward a bit to hear what Heru is telling me. "Breathe with me again............................now on this next exhale leave your breath out until I begin to exhale again. Then breathe my exhalation, my energy in and up through your vagina, your first chakra all the way into your heart. And I will breathe your exhalation from your heart into mine."

A beautiful circle of breath and loving energy is created between us! As the flow strengthens and intensifies, I feel Heru's member thicken and lengthen and my vaginal muscles open and pull him deeper. There is a momentary sense of tearing, and then an exquisite sense of fullness and the longed for internal kiss!

Again, we are still and allow ourselves to fully experience this blissful conversation of our sexual beings and the movement of loving energy circling through us.

The moment arrives when the serpent energies begin again to move strongly upward, and we allow our bodies to move rhythmically together, feeling the serpent's undulating progress through each other's chakras.

My whole body is vibrating and wild cries escape my throat as we move faster and faster.

And then, there is a pause.

Our inner vision opens as we move over the edge and the drops of divine nectar fall from the serpent fangs, we merge in mutual orgasmic ecstasy and taste the divine sweetness.

As we nestle together in the warm afterglow of our ecstatic union and allow the energy to nourish our Ka bodies, I am aware with complete certainty that our child has been conceived and is also being nourished in my womb.

SOPHIA – POSTSCRIPT WITH NIANTHA

I wake up smiling from a very special dream. "Charlie! Guess who came into my dream?"

"Who?"

"Niantha! She gave me a beautiful lapis lazuli stone."

"Wow, the perfect stone to use for an Egyptian connection!"

"Yes. I'm going to my healing room and find my piece of lapis to meditate with."

Charlie and I are married now and we are living in Hot Springs Arkansas. Located over a huge strata of Quartz crystal, Hot Springs is a perfect fit for us as a crystal healer and a shaman. Our experience in Egypt was eight years ago and our journey since then has taken us to many more sacred places and the creation of a great many Columns of Light, as well as lots of personal ups and downs. But that's another story!

Right now I am quite excited to explore this reconnection with Niantha.

I have a beautiful piece of lapis lazuli among my wind element stones on the long table where I have all my healing stones arranged. I pick it up and enjoy looking at its beautiful deep blue color and sparkling flecks of pyrite. I sit and hold it in my left hand and sink into a meditative state. I tune into the stone, allowing its energy to soak into my hand and move up my arm to fill my heart, my body, my whole energy field.

Then, rather unexpectedly, I find the lapis energy taking me deep into my 2nd chakra, my womb. I experience it as the energy of Isis and the inner knowledge of my true woman self as Her manifestation. I am in the cave of my womb, in a very comforting almost darkness, the darkest blue before full black night. It gradually opens and grows into the vastness of space and eventually becomes full darkness with a multitude of stars.

After some minutes, I become aware of the presence of the masculine form of spirit, Cosmic Consciousness, within my womb, being held by me as my divine feminine Isis self. We meet with so much love. We explode into blissful creation. I am shaking with energy pouring up my djed, my central column.

As I begin to settle and relax into a more calm meditative state, I feel the waves of ecstasy continue to flow through me and out into my Ka body. My whole central column and all my chakras feel awake and open.

I find myself now more present in my inner 3rd eye. My inner vision is fully activated. I witness from Niantha's inner perspective her ecstatic union with Horus, the undulating rise of the serpents through each other's chakras, and then the sublime culmination as the red and white serpentine drops fall from the serpents' mouths to mix in the chalice in the center of the lovers' heads, stimulating the pineal gland and creating waves of celestial bliss!

"Dear Sophie, I share this experience of the sex magic of Isis with you as my wedding gift to you and Charlie. My Heru and I had many years of beautiful sacred sexual experiences practicing the alchemies we learned from the Hathors. Although our opportunities to be together physically were rare, we used our spiritual energies to stay in communication and often had blissful encounters in the higher dimensions."

"Thank you so much Niantha. What a wonderful gift! Charlie and I are just beginning to explore our sacred sexuality and want to learn more about what was taught in the Egyptian Mystery Schools. I love that our connection with you and Horus and the Hathors will be so much a part of our lives in this way."

One day, weeks later, I am putting my stones back on their shelf after a healing. As I pick up my lapis lazuli, which I had used on my client's 3rd eye, I notice a whiff of frankincense and lotus flowers. Was Niantha calling to me again?

Holding the lapis in my hand, I begin vocal toning both to clear the stone from the client's energy and to connect with the sound of the Hathor music, which connects Niantha and I to each other and to them.

I really get into the singing and begin to experience the sound of another voice joining mine, guiding me into even more resonant and joyous tones.

Soon I find myself in a vision of the Hathor Temple at Dendera.

"Sophie, come sit with me here in our favorite place the Hathor Temple in Dendera. Now you see me as an older woman, more your own age."

"Thank you for coming to share yourself with me again dear Niantha."

"I have much to be grateful for in my long life. My connection with you beloved Sophie played a crucial role in the early days of my relationship with Horus and his Hathor family. I learned so much from them of the power of the heart, of love and sound. I learned the great gifts of my physical body, ka body, my Ba (celestial soul) and how to raise my Djed through meditation and sacred sexuality."

"My sister priestesses have helped me to share this wisdom through our mystery school. The first to complete this training was my dear son Baraka, son of Horus. Our "blessed gift" Baraka went on to become a beloved king of our land, the first to carry the staff engraved with the eye of Horus, just as was predicted by my long ago vision in the temple before I went into hiding."

"I loved being a mother—all of it: pregnancy, birth, and all the phases of growing child and young adult. My Hathor guides were there to offer me suggestions and support at every stage. I was only sad that my beloved Horus and I had only one child. It has been my great joy to spend time with the women of my community and to be intimately involved in helping and teaching them about what I learned about midwifery and healing and a woman's spiritual journey."

"Oh, Niantha, I can almost see images of you sharing your wise, healing and loving presence with everyone in Dendera. No wonder you will be honored not only as Queen Mother, but as the Goddess Hator herself!"

"Thank you, Sophie. In parting, I want to pass on a message from the Hathors. They are asking you to write about and share your experiences with them. The Hathor messages are very needed by humanity in your time. They love you. I love you. We are always accessible to you. Use sound, your special stones, and your heart to call us."

FINAL MESSAGE FROM THE HATHORS

Our most important message to humanity is to honor and spend time in your heart.

Bringing your awareness to rest in your heart by placing your hands there is a wonderful practice.

All answers can be found in the heart. It is your most precious human organ—the portal of direct linkage to cosmic awareness.

Your heart will help you with self-healing and cultivating the state of being necessary to make all of life's transitions as well as the evolution required in the process of ascension.

Being fully present in your heart gives you immense expansiveness and the understanding of the true Oneness of all Creation.

Love yourself and all creation by perceiving, speaking and acting through your compassionate heart.

AUTHOR'S AFTERWORD

The story you have just read is fiction. However, as you may have guessed, it is inspired by experiences from my life. For example, I really did take a sacred journey to Egypt and I did meet my beloved husband Bruce "Gentle Bear" Durward on that trip. Also, the Hathors have been and continue to be important spiritual guides for me. I experienced their presence as an active part of my writing process.

I view the Hathors as an ascended civilization of interdimensional beings. They feel they are our elder brothers and sisters in consciousness and part of their continued evolution is to help humankind, which they have been doing for millennia. In ancient Egypt they worked through the cult of the sky goddess Hator. They are masters of sound and energy. My view of the Hathors is cultivated from my own experiences and from the information channeled by Tom Kenyon.

Because it was instrumental in my decision to write this book, I would like to share an experience in which my Hathor guides transported me back to their temple at Dendera several years after my original visit.

I was deep within my morning meditation when inside my head I heard "we want to take you somewhere."

I agreed and felt myself swept off to Egypt, to the Temple of the Hathors at Dendera. It was just as I remembered from my visit there five years ago. There was the awesome, beautifully preserved temple within the grand Dendera complex set in the desert not far from the Nile River. As I walked up the steps, I saw the huge columns and looked up to the beloved Hathor faces atop each one.

I happily entered and immediately felt the rush of loving, healing energy that just made me want to sit and gaze up at the Hathor which graced the top of each of the beautifully carved columns-- rows and rows of them! I found myself connecting with my heart and focusing on the heart meditation they had taught me in my initiation with them. What a gift!

But that wasn't all. Next, I was told to stop trying and simply let go and receive. As I did so, I experienced myself being glided through the entire grand hall of Hathor pillars---weaving in, out, around and through them all! I was gliding faster and faster until I had a slight sense of vertigo. Then it was complete. I felt very good and clear--sure that I had received a profound, if mysterious, healing.

It was also communicated to me that, using guided visualization, I would bring others here to the Hathor Temple on their own virtual healing journeys. Thank you my dear Hathors.

After I had the above experience, I began communicating with the Hathors more frequently. I would get messages in my meditation and in my journaling. I found that if I listened to one of Tom Kenyon's recordings of Hathor singing through his amazing multi-octave voice, I felt their presence very strongly and received many clear messages.

Not only did they encourage and help me to write this book, but they also helped me to create and begin practicing what I call Hathor Healing. It incorporates virtual healing journeys to the Hathor Temple of Healing with powerful Hathor Heart and Sound Resonance augmented by the use of crystals to amplify, channel and program the healing energy. Hathor Healing addresses one's Khat (physical) body, Ka (energy) body and Ba (celestial soul) for clearing, healing and spiritual evolution. The practice is designed for in-person sessions or long-distance healings. I have 15 years experience as a certified crystal resonance therapist and find that these 2 practices overlap and complement each other very well.

For me Hathor Healing is exciting and still evolving even though its roots may be ancient. Recently, I was very concerned about my mother who was having a bit of a healing crisis after a fall. Although I was far from her physically, I was guided by the Hathors to bring my mother virtually into the Hathor Healing Temple and float her in her bed through the rows of pillars. Because she loves me and trusts me, she would come easily while she is sleeping. Bathed in the Hathor healing energy, her pain would be eased in a way that is for the highest good. I was also able to imagine using my hands on her to help release the trauma and to calm, ground and rebalance her chakras. The new realization was that also this process could allow her Ka to be gently and incrementally stepped down over many sessions, allowing her to leave her body at the end of her life in an easy, gradual, graceful way. I felt blessed and grateful that yes there was something I could do for her from so far away.

If you would like to find out more about the Hathor Healing modality or schedule a session, please contact me through my website **www.crystalsoflight.com.**

QUAN YIN, ARK OF THE COVENANT, & THE HOLY CELL TOWERS was co-authored with Bruce before our marriage under the name Nia Kallhof. You may want to check it out if you want to read more about our adventures together.

Made in the USA
Columbia, SC
27 November 2024